Sneezy Snatchers and other villains

Compiled by Pat Edwards

Acknowledgements

The author's agents for the story 'Sneezy Snatcher and Sammy Small' from *A Book of Giants* by Ruth Manning-Sanders (pub Methuen); Penguin Books Ltd for the poems 'Who's scared now?' from p.28 *Songs For My Dog and Other People* by Max Fatchen (Kestrel Books, 1980) Copyright © 1980 by Max Fatchen and 'I often meet a monster' from p. 11 *Wry Rhymes for Troublesome Times* by Max Fatchen (Kestrel Books, 1983) Copyright © by Max Fatchen 1983; Penguin Books Australia Ltd for the poems 'Bad Fairy' and 'Victor R.I.P' from *In the Garden of Badthings* by Doug MacLeod; Annick Press Ltd., Ontario, Canada for 'The Paper Bag Princess' by Robert N. Munsch; Ward Lock Educational Co. Ltd for the story 'The Girl and the Witch' from *Short Tales 1* by Geoffrey Summerfield. Pages 50-51 were written by Bill Boyle.

We are grateful to the following for permission to reproduce photographs: Barnaby's Picture Library p.51 above right (photo: Harold Oldroyal); Bradford Art Galleries and Museums p.51 below right; Beamish North of England Open Air Museum p.50 below; Michael Holford p.50 above; Jorvik Viking Centre, York Archaeological Trust p.51 above left.

Illustrators, other than those acknowledged with each story, include: Anni Axeworthy pp.16-17; Waldemar Buczński pp.8-15; Rowena Cory and Chris Johnston pp.36-49, 64; Terry Denton pp.4-5; Marjory Gardner pp.30-31; Betty Greenhatch pp.32-33; Rolf Heimann p.62; Cindy Hunnam pp.34-35; Michael Martchenko pp.20-29; Jiri Tibor Novak pp.52-61, 63; Val Sassoon pp.50-51; Gaston Vanzet pp.6-7; David Woodward pp.18-19.

Apple-tree, apple-tree, hide me quick,
Or the witch will come with her big stick,
And then she'll boil and pick my bones,
And bury me under the marble stones.

CONTENTS

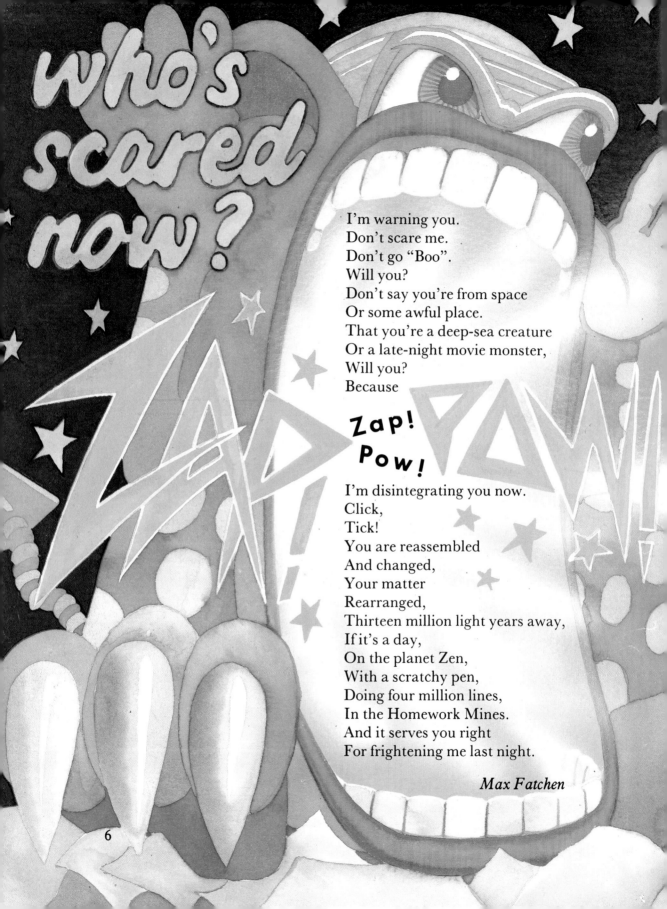

who's scared now?

I'm warning you.
Don't scare me.
Don't go "Boo".
Will you?
Don't say you're from space
Or some awful place.
That you're a deep-sea creature
Or a late-night movie monster,
Will you?
Because

Zap!
Pow!

I'm disintegrating you now.
Click,
Tick!
You are reassembled
And changed,
Your matter
Rearranged,
Thirteen million light years away,
If it's a day,
On the planet Zen,
With a scratchy pen,
Doing four million lines,
In the Homework Mines.
And it serves you right
For frightening me last night.

Max Fatchen

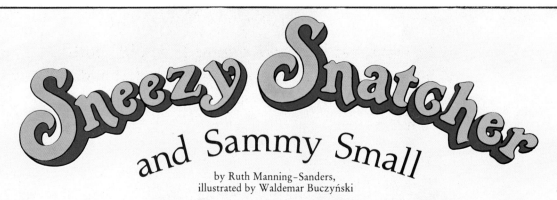

Sneezy Snatcher

and Sammy Small

by Ruth Manning-Sanders,
illustrated by Waldemar Buczyński

Sammy Small's mother went out to do washing for people. One day, before she went, she said, "Sammy, be a good boy, and don't go round the corner of the street."

"Why not?" said Sammy.

"Because, if you do, Sneezy Snatcher will have you," said his mother.

"Who's he?" said Sammy.

"A great big giant," said his mother.

And she pulled the heavy boots on to her feet, to keep them dry whilst she was at the wash-tub, and off she went, *Stumpetty-stump*.

Well, Sammy played round the yard for a bit, and then he got bored, and wandered out into the street.

8

In the street there were three little girls with a skipping-rope. Two were turning, and the third was leisurely skipping, and they were all three singing:

Sneezy Snatcher,
Boy in the pot.
Not bad cold, but some *nice hot!*
Sneezy Snatcher, I'll give 'ee warning,
How many boys have 'ee catched this morning?

9

Then the two little girls twirled the rope fast as fast, and the third little girl skipped like mad, and they all began counting:

"One, two, three, four, five ..." until the skipping girl tripped over the rope. Then one of the turning girls took her place, and she turned, and the song began all over again.

"Why, 'tis nothing but a silly girls' game," said Sammy to himself. "There's not such a person as Sneezy Snatcher. My mammy only said it to frighten me."

And on to the corner of the street he marched, and round the corner he went, bold as brass.

But there *was* such a person as Sneezy Snatcher, and as he happened just then to be waiting round the corner with his sack on his back, he no sooner set eyes on Sammy than he picked him up between his finger and thumb, and dropped him, screeching and squirming, into his sack.

Away he went now to his house, which was a very big one, and into the kitchen, and there he shook Sammy out of the sack.

"Aha!" said he. "Are you a plump boy, or are you a skinny one?"

And he began pinching Sammy's arms and legs, to feel was he fat or wasn't he; because he was so short-sighted that he couldn't tell without feeling.

"Skinny!" said he at last, very disappointed. "We'll have to boil you."

Then he called Mrs Sneezy Snatcher, and in she came out of the back place; and she was a great, fat giantess with a foolish-looking face.

"Dumpty, my sweetheart," said he, "here's a boiling boy. You keep your eye on him, while I go pluck a few herbs to put in the pot."

"All right, Sneezy," said she.

So off he went, and Mrs Sneezy Snatcher stood staring down at Sammy, and Sammy sat staring up at her, and she looked so foolish that Sammy began to feel quite brave.

"Does Mr Sneezy Snatcher always have boys for dinner?" said he.

"When he can catch 'em, my lover," says she.

"Does he only have boys?" said Sammy. "Or does he have pudding as well?"

"Oh, pudding!" said Mrs Sneezy Snatcher. "I do dearly love a bit of pudding, but it's not often we can rise to it. Times is bad for us poor giants."

"My mammy made a great big pudding this very morning," said Sammy.

"I wish I was your mammy, then!" said Mrs Sneezy Snatcher.

"A pudding as big as your head," said Sammy.

"Ah-h!" sighed Mrs Sneezy Snatcher.

"With raisins and currants in it," said Sammy.

"Don't, don't!" cried Mrs Sneezy Snatcher.

"And I know she'd give you some," said Sammy. "Shall I run home and ask her?"

"My days, how kind!" said Mrs Sneezy Snatcher. "Yes, go, there's my handsome. But mind you come back in time to be boiled."

"I'll run like the wind," said Sammy.

And run like the wind he did. But he didn't come back to be boiled.

Traditional English story

How to recognise a *Sneezy Snatcher**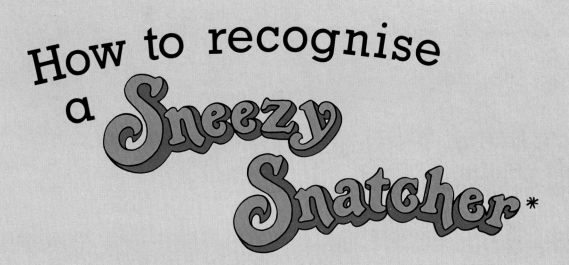

1 He's a **giant.**

2 He carries a sack for putting people in.

3 He probably sneezes a lot.

4 He likes eating boiled boys and puddings.

5 His wife is easy to trick, so bright boys can usually get away.

NB If you're a girl, be careful. Sneezy Snatchers probably like them fried!

* Better carry this list with you.

I often meet a MONSTER

I often meet a monster
While deep in sleep at night;
And I confess to some distress.
It gives me quite a fright.
But then again I wonder.
I have this thought, you see.
Do little sleeping monsters scream
Who dream
Of meeting me?

Max Fatchen

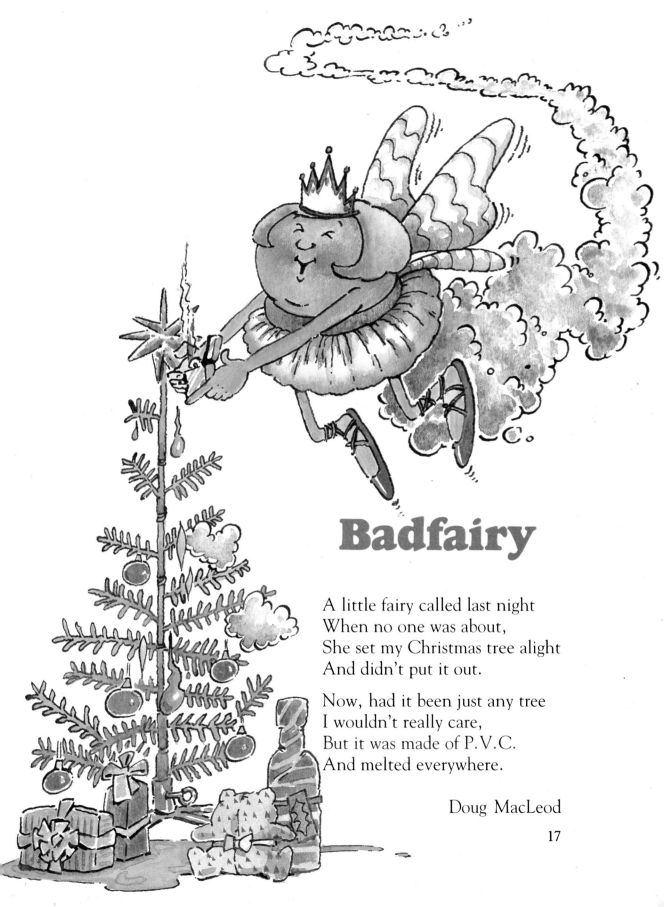

Badfairy

A little fairy called last night
When no one was about,
She set my Christmas tree alight
And didn't put it out.

Now, had it been just any tree
I wouldn't really care,
But it was made of P.V.C.
And melted everywhere.

Doug MacLeod

Staying alive when out and about

Always use a pedestrian crossing if there is one.

Look both ways before crossing a road.

Never play on the road.

18

The Paper Bag Princess

by Robert N. Munsch,
illustrated by Michael Martchenko

Elizabeth was a beautiful princess. She lived in a castle
and had expensive princess clothes.

She was going to marry a prince named Ronald.

Unfortunately, a dragon smashed her castle, burned all her clothes with his fiery breath, and carried off Prince Ronald.

Elizabeth decided to chase the dragon and get Ronald back.

She looked everywhere for something to wear but the only thing she could find that was not burnt was a paper bag. So she put on the paper bag and followed the dragon.

He was easy to follow because he left a trail of burnt forests and horses' bones.

Finally, Elizabeth came to a cave with a large door that had a huge knocker on it.

She took hold of the knocker and banged on the door.

The dragon stuck his nose out of the door and said, "Well, a princess! I love to eat princesses, but I have already eaten a whole castle today. I am a very busy dragon. Come back tomorrow."

He slammed the door so fast that Elizabeth almost got her nose caught.

Elizabeth grabbed the knocker and banged on the door again.

The dragon stuck his nose out of the door and said, "Go away. I love to eat princesses, but I have already eaten a whole castle today. I am a very busy dragon. Come back tomorrow."

"Wait," shouted Elizabeth. "Is it true that you are the smartest and fiercest dragon in the whole world?"

"Yes," said the dragon.

"Is it true," said Elizabeth, "that you can burn up ten forests with your fiery breath?"

"Oh, yes," said the dragon, and he took a huge, deep breath and breathed out so much fire that he burnt up fifty forests.

25

"Fantastic," said Elizabeth, and the dragon took another huge breath and breathed out so much fire that he burnt up one hundred forests.

"Magnificent," said Elizabeth, and the dragon took another huge breath, but this time nothing came out.

The dragon didn't even have enough fire left to cook a meatball.

Elizabeth said, "Dragon, is it true that you can fly around the world in just ten seconds?"

"Why, yes," said the dragon and jumped up and flew all the way around the world in just ten seconds.

He was very tired when he got back, but Elizabeth shouted, "Fantastic, do it again!"

So the dragon jumped up and flew around the whole world in just twenty seconds.

When he got back he was too tired to talk and he lay down and went straight to sleep.

Elizabeth whispered very softly, "Hey, dragon." The dragon didn't move at all.

She lifted up the dragon's ear and put her head right inside. She shouted as loud as she could, "Hey, dragon!"

The dragon was so tired he didn't even move.

Elizabeth walked right over the dragon and opened the door to the cave.

There was Prince Ronald.

He looked at her and said, "Elizabeth, you are a mess! You smell like ashes, your hair is all tangled and you are wearing a dirty old paper bag. Come back when you are dressed like a real princess."

"Ronald," said Elizabeth. "Your clothes are really pretty and your hair is very neat. You look like a real prince, but you are a toad."

They didn't get married after all.

Dragon words

FIERY BREATH FIERY

POISONOUS TIP POISONOUS TIP POISONOUS TIP POISONOUS TIP POISONOUS TIP POISONOUS TIP POISONOUS TIP POISONOUS TIP POISONOUS TIP POISONOUS TIP POISONOUS TIP POISONOUS TIP POISONOUS TIP POISON

HAUNCHES HAUNCHES HAUNCHES HAUNCHES HAUNCHES HAUNCHES HAUNCHES

SCALY BODY GREEN SCALY BODY GREEN SCALY BODY GREEN SCALY BODY GREEN SCALY BODY GREEN

SOFT YELLOW BELLY SOFT YELLOW BELLY SOFT YELLOW BELLY SOFT YELLOW BELLY SOFT YELLOW BELLY

SHARP HORNY CLAWS SHARP HORNY CLAWS SHARP HORNY CLAWS

GREEN SCALY TAIL GREEN SCALY TAIL GREEN SCALY TAIL GREEN SCALY TAIL GREEN SCALY TAIL GREEN SCALY TAIL GREEN SCALY TAIL GREEN SCALY TAIL GREEN SCALY TAIL GREEN SCALY TAIL GREEN SCALY TAIL GREEN SCALY TAIL GREEN SCALY TAIL GREEN SCALY TAIL GREEN SCALY

SHARP HORNY CLAWS SHARP HORNY CLAWS SHARP HORNY LEG

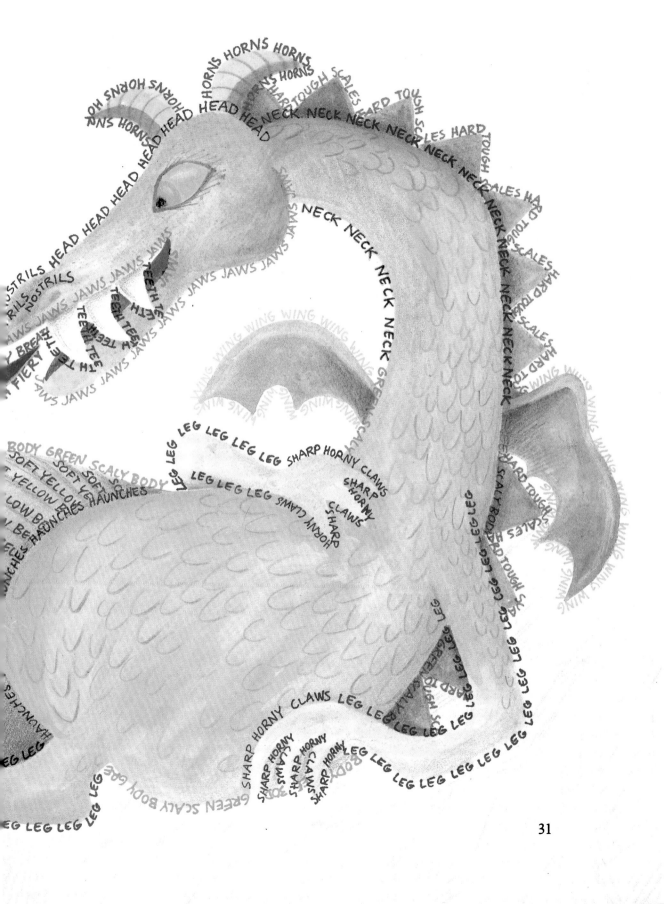

Fascinating facts about dragons

You make good toast.

Our word for dragon comes to us from the Greek word *drakon* which meant 'to watch'.
That's because in old stories dragons usually watched over or guarded someone or something — like a princess!

I wish someone could rescue me.

At least twelve saints were dragon-slayers, but the one we know best is St George.

Artists long ago thought dragons were like crocodiles with wings and that they had tails like serpents.

Ancient Britons and the Welsh used the dragon on their standard and they called their leader in war PENDRAGON. The Welsh still have a red dragon on their flag.

I'm a British dragon.

龍

Means "dragon" in Chinese.

Most British dragons were WORMS like the ones found in stories from Norway, Sweden and Denmark.

Winged dragons have flames coming out of their mouths, but Worms' breath is poisonous. Both kinds are scaly, like to live in pools or wells and love eating maidens. All the stories say that they like to hoard treasure and are very hard to kill.

Chinese people believe dragons bring good luck. That's why you'll see dragons in their New Year Parade.

None of the dragons was ever real, but they might have been imagined long ago by people who found the remains of prehistoric monsters.

33

Saint George's Day

23 April

Keep away from my lunch!

Who was Saint George?

The stories say that George was a Christian Knight of Cappadocia around AD 300.*
One day he visited a town where the people were terrified of a dragon that ate only human beings. The princess had been chosen as the dragon's next meal, but George killed the dragon and saved her from a horrible end. He refused to take any reward, but asked the townspeople to all become Christians.

* AD stands for Anno Domini – "in the year of the Lord". Our calendar counts the years before Christ's birth (BC) and since Christ's birth (AD).

Why is he remembered?

English knights heard about
St George and so King Edward
the Third made him England's
special saint.
He's also patron saint of the
Greek army.

Good to see you George!

Why should we know about him?

St George is the patron saint of England
and his cross is on on the English flag.
The cross of St George also makes up part
of the Union Jack which is Britain's flag.

35

The little girl and the witch

by Geoffrey Summerfield, illustrated by Rowena Cory and Chris Johnston

Once upon a time, there was a girl whose parents were very poor. "Mother, let me go away and find work somewhere," she said one day.

"It's a sad day when you have to leave home, but beggars can't be choosers," her mother said. "So go with my blessings."

She wrapped all her belongings in an old cloth, and away she went. She walked all over the first town she came to, knocking on doors, and asking for work, but nobody wanted her. So she sat down, ate her bread and cheese and then she set off again.

Soon she came to an old house. The door
stood open, and there was no one to be seen.
"Is anybody there?" she called out, but no
answer came.

So she tiptoed into the kitchen, where she
saw a great oven, with a hot roaring fire
underneath it. She went to the oven to warm
her hands, and suddenly she heard voices:
"Little girl, little girl, take us out, take us
out. We've been baking seven long years,
and no-one has come to take us out."

So she took the loaves out of the oven, put
them on the table, and went to see if she
could find anyone.

In a shed, at the back of the house, she found a cow, which said: "Little girl, little girl, milk me, milk me! Seven long years I've been waiting, and no-one has come to milk me."

So she milked the cow, catching the milk in a great pail that stood close by, then she went on to explore the orchard.

As soon as she was in the orchard, an apple tree whose branches were almost breaking with the weight of its apples said, "Little girl, little girl, help me shake off my fruit. There's such a load, my branches almost break."

So the girl shook all the apples off the tree, and took some with her back into the house.

She walked into the kitchen, and there, to her surprise, stood an old witch. "And what can I do for you?" said the witch.

"I have left home to look for work. My parents are poor and can't keep me."

"Oh, that's a sad tale," said the witch. "You had better come and work for me."

"Is there work here for me?"

"You can clean the house, and sweep the floor, and polish the doorknobs on the door. You can dust the shelves and bake my bread, and polish the bedknobs on my bed. You can wash the windows, make the fire, and always be truthful, never a liar. Is that to your liking?"

"I'll do all that, and more besides."

"But one thing you must never do. You must promise never to look up the chimney."

"I promise. Cross my heart," said the girl.

41

Next day, the witch went out on witch-business, looking for toads and bats and spiders' webs, while the girl did the housework. And she sang as she worked:

"I must clean the house, and sweep the floor
And polish the doorknobs on the door.
I must dust the shelves and bake the bread,
And polish the bedknobs on the bed."

She worked downstairs; then she worked upstairs; then she came down again, and cleaned the windows.

She was tired by this time, so she made herself a cup of tea and sat by the fire. The flames were disappearing up the chimney, bright gold and red vanishing into the black soot. She leaned forward to see where the flames were going . . .

Suddenly two great bags of gold fell down the chimney. They bounced off the coals and onto the floor, so quickly that they didn't have time to burn or even singe at the edges.

She bent down and picked them up, then she remembered what the old witch had said: "Never look up the chimney!"

"What have I done?" she cried. "And what will she do to me?" Even as she spoke, she heard the latch on the gate go clickety-click, and knew that the witch was coming back.

So she snatched up the bags and rushed
out through the back door and into the
orchard:

"*Apple-tree, apple-tree, hide me quick,*
Or the witch will come with her big stick,
And then she'll boil and pick my bones,
And bury me under the marble stones."

So the apple tree hid her in its hundreds of
branches and thousands of leaves.

No sooner was she hidden, than the old
witch came tottering out to the tree and said:

"Apple-tree, apple-tree
You must tell what you see!
Have you seen a girl in rags,
Stealing away with my money-bags?"

The apple-tree answered, "No, mother, not
for seven long years."

Then the old witch staggered off into the house, and as soon as she was gone inside, the girl climbed down out of the tree, to make her escape. But she was just passing the shed, when she heard the witch coming out again.

She rushed into the cow-shed, and said to the cow:

"Gentle cow, please hide me here.
The witch is after me, I fear.
She'll cook my flesh in her great pot
And throw my bones away, to rot!"

So the cow moved over, and she climbed in
behind and was hidden. It was just in the
nick of time, for the old witch came hobbling
in, and said:

> *"Listen to me, you lazy cow,*
> *Tell the truth, and tell me now.*
> *Where's the girl who stole my gold?*
> *Speak out now, quickly, clear and bold."*

But the cow answered, "I've not seen her
for seven long years." Then the witch went
up the garden, and the girl tip-toed back into
the house to collect her belongings, so that
she could run away and never come back.
She was just slipping through the kitchen
when she heard the old witch coming back in.

"I'll be caught!" she thought, so she hid behind the sideboard. When she peeped out, she saw the witch leaning over and peering into the oven. So she jumped out, gave the old witch a good push right into the oven, slammed the oven door, and made sure it was tight.

Then she wrapped up her few belongings in an old tablecloth and went off home with the two bags of gold. As for the old witch, she's still cooped up in the oven, and if anybody is ever foolish enough to open the door, they'll be sorry.

It's my home
The North of England

The north of England is more than just factories and cities! Visitors come to see our beautiful lakes, mountains and moors.

Blackpool is the main holiday resort in the north of England. Its tower (160 metres high), three piers, trams and illuminations attract many thousands of visitors each year.

If you visit the museum in Beamish, County Durham, you can learn about coal mining. You can look round the coal mine shown here.

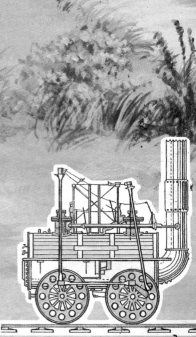

George Stephenson's early steam engine, *Locomotion*, which pulled the world's first passenger train, can be seen at Darlington's Railway Museum.

Guy Fawkes, who tried to blow up the Houses of Parliament, was born in York in 1570. If you go to York, you can see the Viking City at the Jorvik Centre, and the National Railway Museum.

a Viking family preparing a meal

The seaports of Hull, Scarborough and Whitby were the homes of the North Sea fishing fleet. In the past, this coast had many shipwrecks and people could make a living from selling the things that were washed up on the beach.

Whitby

Bradford Industrial Museum

Have you tried one of our northern specialities? Black pudding – lovely!

The beautiful lakes and mountains of the Lake District were formed millions of years ago during the Ice Age. Today, this area is popular with walkers and climbers from many countries who come here on holiday.

Leeds and Bradford are two of the biggest industrial cities in the north. In the past, they were centres for wool. The sheep were raised on the nearby Pennines, which also provided the soft water needed for washing the wool. You can see how a mill worked at the Bradford Industrial Museum. Today, much of the wool used for making cloth is imported.

The old woman who lost her dumpling

Long ago and far away in Japan there lived an old woman. Every day she made dumplings for her dinner.

One day a dumpling slipped out of her hand. Down it plopped, into a hole in the dusty floor of her kitchen.

"Bother," said the old woman, and put her hand down the hole to pick it up.

"Bother," she said again when she could not find the dumpling. "Where has it gone?"

So she put her arm into the hole. She could feel nothing under the floor. Where was that dumpling?

52

Then the old woman put her head into the hole to see what was going on. Whoosh! The earth fell away and she tumbled right in.

She tumbled and tumbled, down, down, down to another world. It *looked* like her world. She was standing on a road just like the one that went past her own doorway. She could see fields of rice in the distance. But there were no people.

The old woman was brave and determined. She had come to this place to find her dumpling, so find it she would. She dusted herself down, tidied her clothes and stepped out along the road. As she went, she called, "Rolling, rumbling, where's my dumpling?"

Many steps later, the old woman came upon a stone statue by the side of the road.

"Have you seen a dumpling rolling down the road?" she asked the statue.

"Indeed I have," it replied. "But do not follow it. Your dumpling was rolling towards the castle of the giant who eats people."

"Nonsense!" said the old woman. She continued on her way, calling, "Rolling, tumbling, where's my dumpling?"

54

Many more steps later, the old woman passed another stone statue by the side of the road.

"Have you seen a dumpling rolling down this road?"

"It passed by some time ago. Beware, it was rolling towards the castle of the giant who eats people."

"Rubbish!" said the old woman. She walked on, calling, "Rolling, bumping, where's my dumpling?"

Many, many more steps later she found a third statue by the side of the road.

"Have you seen a dumpling rolling down this road?"

"Sshh. Forget about your dumpling. Here comes the giant. Hide behind me and be quiet."

The giant clopped down the road, shaking the trees as he passed. He came to the statue and sniffed. He sniffed, then sniffed again.

"A human being has been here, Tell me, statue, is she near?"

55

The old woman was not a bit afraid. In fact, she thought the giant looked rather funny. He looked so funny that she started giggling—silently at first, then louder and louder.

Of course, the giant heard her. He reached out his great hand and grasped the old woman around the waist.

"Do not hurt her," pleaded the stone statue. "She has done you no harm."

"To please you, I will not eat her for dinner," replied the giant. "Instead, she will make my dinner. She will become my cook."

So the giant carried the old woman to the end of the road. All the way, she looked from side to side, searching for her lost dumpling, but she never found it.

At last they came to a wide river. On the shore was a boat big enough for a giant. The giant stepped in and rowed the old woman across to his castle on the other side.

There were two other giants living in the castle. The giant carried the old woman into his huge kitchen and gave her a wooden spoon.

"Now you will cook dinner for me and my friends," he said in his loud booming voice. "Put only one grain of rice in the pot. Stir it with this spoon and the grain will grow. One grain will feed us all."

The old woman laughed again, but she did as the giant ordered. As she stirred, the grain of rice became two ... four ... eight ... sixteen. After a few minutes the huge pot was full.

The old woman stayed with the giant and his friends for many months. Every day she used the magic spoon to turn one grain of rice into enough for all of them. She was treated well. The giants did not hurt her and she often amused them with her stories.

But as time passed, the old woman became homesick. She longed to be back in her own little house cooking her dumplings. One evening, when she went to the kitchen to cook the giants' dinner, she decided to run away.

She slipped the magic spoon into her belt and sneaked down to the river. There, on the bank, was the boat. With all her strength, the old woman slowly pushed it into the water and started rowing. It was hard work indeed!

It was not long before the hungry giants discovered that the old woman had got away. They ran down to the river. There, in the middle of the stream, was the old woman rowing with all her might.

Now, although these giants were very big and sometimes quite fierce, they did not know how to swim.

"Drink, drink up all the water," called the giant who had brought the old woman to them many months ago.

So the three giants knelt on the river bank and slurped and slurped. As they drank, the water in the river fell lower and lower. The old woman kept rowing until there was no more water for her to row in.

As the giants waded through the mud to reach her, the old woman started making faces at them. She looked so funny that all the giants burst out laughing.

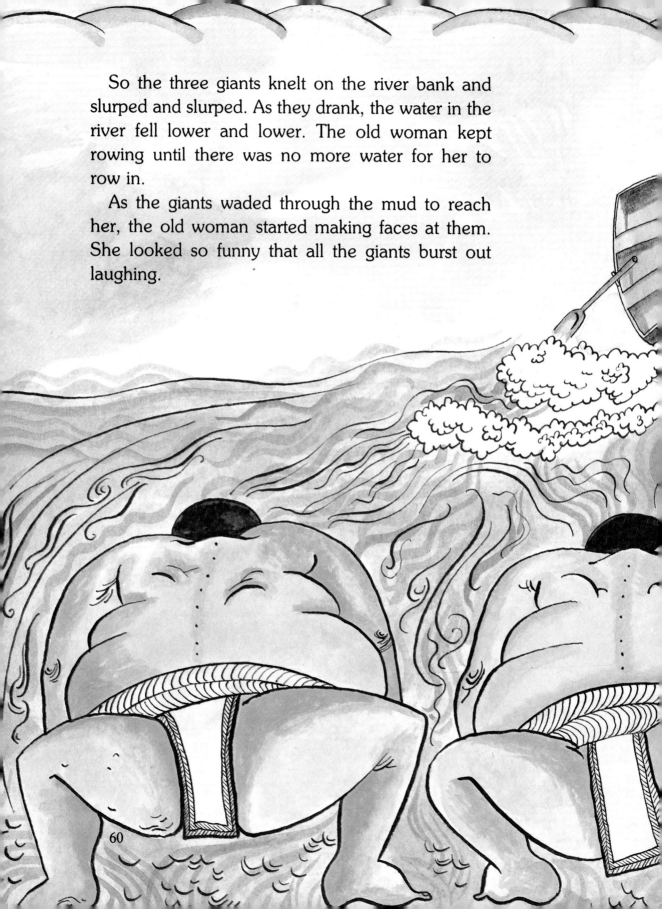

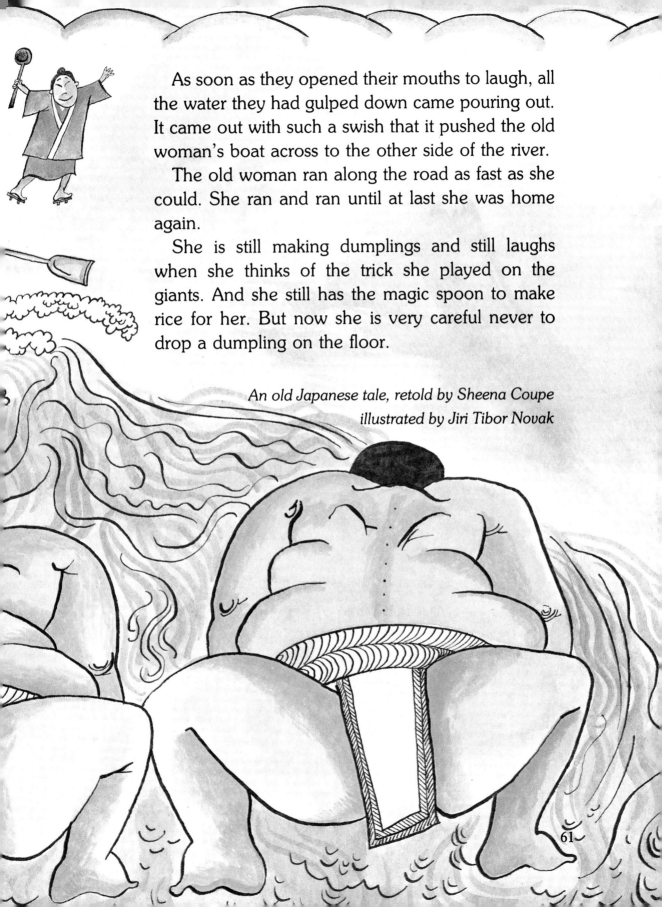

As soon as they opened their mouths to laugh, all the water they had gulped down came pouring out. It came out with such a swish that it pushed the old woman's boat across to the other side of the river.

The old woman ran along the road as fast as she could. She ran and ran until at last she was home again.

She is still making dumplings and still laughs when she thinks of the trick she played on the giants. And she still has the magic spoon to make rice for her. But now she is very careful never to drop a dumpling on the floor.

An old Japanese tale, retold by Sheena Coupe
illustrated by Jiri Tibor Novak

And everyone got away except Victor!

VICTOR R.I.P.

Remember the fate of Victor McGage who ventured too close to the reptile cage. A hungry old snake took a liking to Victor

He was delicious!

So, now he's a lump in a boa-constrictor.

Doug MacLeod

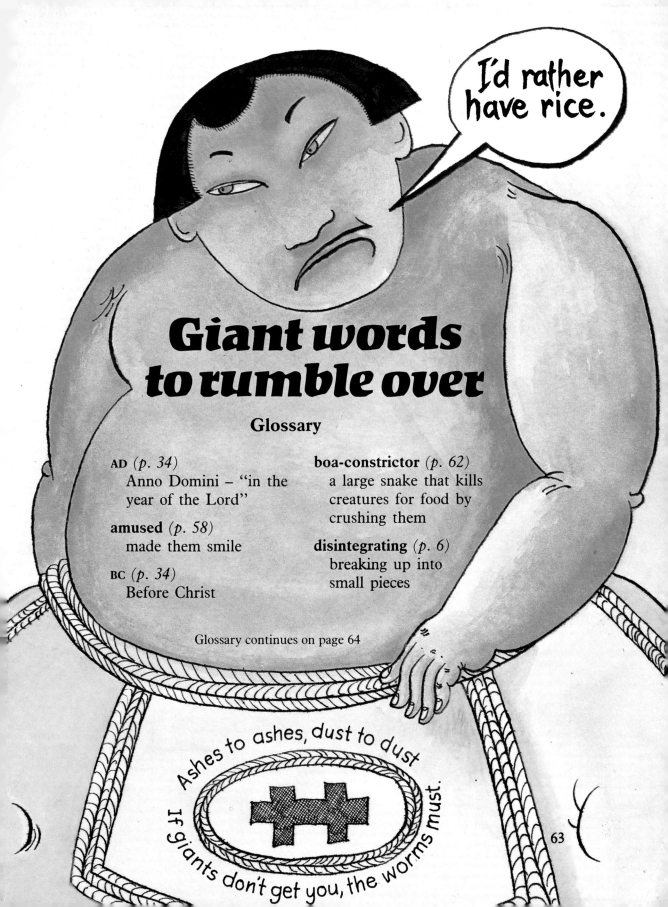

I'd rather have rice.

Giant words to rumble over

Glossary

AD (*p. 34*)
Anno Domini – "in the year of the Lord"

amused (*p. 58*)
made them smile

BC (*p. 34*)
Before Christ

boa-constrictor (*p. 62*)
a large snake that kills creatures for food by crushing them

disintegrating (*p. 6*)
breaking up into small pieces

Glossary continues on page 64

Ashes to ashes, dust to dust

If giants don't get you, the worms must.

dumpling (*p. 52*)
a lump of boiled dough

'ee (*p. 9*)
you

leisurely (*p. 9*)
in no hurry

mammy (*p. 10*)
mummy

pail (*p. 39*)
bucket

patron saint (*p. 35*)
a saint who looks after
a group of people or
a place

reassembled (*p. 6*)
put together again

serpents (*p. 32*)
large snakes

singe (*p. 44*)
to burn just a little

slurped (*p. 60*)
drank quickly and
noisily

squirming (*p. 10*)
twisting about
like a worm

twirled (*p. 10*)
turned round
quickly

Apple-tree, apple-tree
You must tell me what you see
Have you seen a girl in rags,
Stealing away with my money-bags?